WHIZZ-KI
C000301567
CRUSH
SWEET
YAWN
WHIZZ
SNAP!
TINY'S
ICES

CHEERS!
GRUB
SUPER PUSH!
CHIP-ITES
SD
RASP!
BREAK!
OOER!
RENT SCORE

The Best of
WHIZZER™
and
CHIPS™
Annual
CHIPS is inside
HEAP BRAVE

Welcome to the Best of Whizzer and Chips Annual! We hope you have fun with the Chip-ites and Whizzer-kids.

Do keep your eyes open, as sometimes they appear in each other's comic strips!

EGMONT

The Best of Whizzer and Chips Annual first published in 2014
by Egmont UK Limited, The Yellow Building, 1 Nicholas Road, London W11 4AN

This title features stories, jokes and activities from Whizzer and Chips Annuals dated 1971-1985.
Please note: Some of the material used in this title is exceedingly rare, so the print quality may vary.

classiccomics.egmont.co.uk

ISBN 978 1 4052 7336 7
57318/1
Printed in Italy

What's Inside ...

SID'S
SNAKE

SID
I'M FROZEN STIFF! I HOPE SID LEAVES ME ALONE FOR A WHILE!
CHEEK! THAT'S MY PLACE!

COME ON, SLIPPY! IT'S TOO EARLY TO LAY AROUND SNOOZING!
OH, NO... I HATE THAT MUSIC!
SID

I'M OFF!
WAIL
ZOOM!

IT'S FREEZING OUTSIDE! I'LL HAVE TO FIND SOMEWHERE TO HIDE INDOORS!

A FEW MINUTES LATER...
YEEOW! HE'S FOUND ME ALREADY!
HA, HA — I KNEW YOU'D BE IN HERE WRAPPED ROUND THAT HOT WATER TANK!

I'LL SLIP UP THE PIPE!
HEY! WHERE ARE YOU OFF TO NOW?

UP IN THE ATTIC...
ALL I'VE GOT TO DO IS FIND A HOT WATER PIPE AND WRAP MYSELF AROUND IT!

BUT...
TH-TH-THERE'S A B-BIG B-B-BURST IN THE P-PIPE, SID!
WHAT? HANG ON— I'LL GET MY DAD!

ONE HOUR LATER...
WHERE'S THE LEAK, MATE?
IN THE ATTIC!
PLEASE HURRY... POOR SLIPPY!
I. FIXIT PLUMBER

THIRTY MINUTES LATER...
GOOD JOB YOUR SNAKE WRAPPED HIMSELF ROUND THAT PIPE — SAVED YOU A LOT OF FLOODING!
POOR SLIPPY'S AS STIFF AS A POST!

DON'T WORRY, SLIPPY, AS SOON AS YOU HAVE THAWED OUT YOU CAN CURL UP IN FRONT OF THE FIRE!
AND AS A REWARD I'LL MAKE SURE SID DOESN'T DISTURB YOU!
SID

CHIPS

SHINER

TAKE THESE FLOWERS TO THE DOCTOR, SHINER! AND DON'T GET INTO ANY FIGHTS ON THE WAY, THE DOCTOR DOESN'T LIKE BOYS FIGHTING!
OKAY, MUM!

CAN'T STOP TO FIGHT, BOYS, I'VE GOT TO DELIVER THESE FLOWERS TO THE DOCTOR!
YAH! CISSY!

THESE FLOWERS ARE FROM MY MOTHER, SIR!
OH, YES! THEY'RE TO BRIGHTEN UP THE WAITING ROOM —DO COME IN, SHINER!

WILL YOU GET THAT VASE OFF THE MANTLEPIECE FOR ME, SHINER?
CERTAINLY, DOCTOR!

OH, MY GOODNESS! THE POOR LAD HAS HURT HIMSELF!
OUCH!
BONK!
TRIP!

I'M AFRAID YOU'VE GOT A BLACK EYE!
THINK NOTHING OF IT, DOC!

IT'LL SOON CLEAR UP! HERE'S TEN PENCE FOR BEING SUCH A BRAVE BOY!
COO! THANKS, DOCTOR!
PAT! PAT!

BUT, LATER...
YOU'LL GO STRAIGHT TO BED, SHINER! FANCY TELLING ME FIBS ABOUT GETTING A BLACK EYE AT THE DOCTOR'S!
COO! WHEN I'M TELLING THE TRUTH NOBODY BELIEVES ME!

SAMMY SHRINK

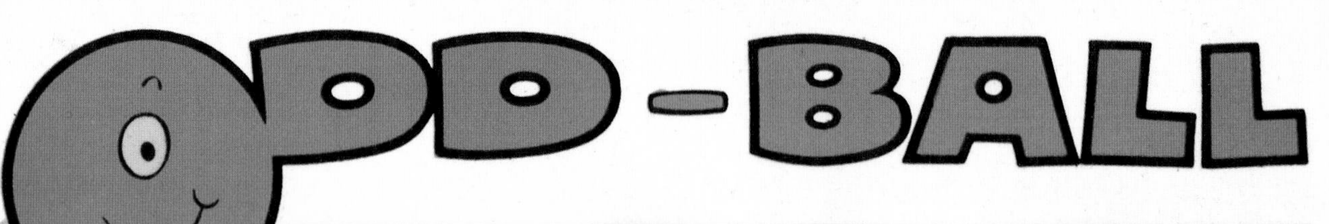
ODD-BALL

WE'LL VISIT AUNT DAISY, ODD-BALL—SHE HASN'T BEEN WELL LATELY!

SNIFF! HOW NICE TO SEE THE TWO OF YOU!
I HOPE YOU'RE FEELING BETTER TODAY, AUNT DAISY!

DING-A-LING
THERE'S SOMEONE AT THE DOOR—I'LL GO!
DON'T BOTHER—SOME YOUNG SCAMP HAS BEEN RINGING THAT BELL AND RUNNING AWAY ALL AFTERNOON!

SO...
THAT'S FINE, ODD-BALL—NOW WE'LL PUT A STOP TO THAT MONKEY'S TRICKS!

COR! THERE'S A NICE NEW BELL FOR ME TO RING!

HA, HA! IT DOESN'T PAY TO PULL ODD-BALL'S LEG!
TUG
STRETCH
WOW!
THUD

NOW ODD-BALL IS PULLING HIM!
AARGH!
YANK
CRUNK

GROAN! I MUST BE IMAGINING THINGS!

HELP! NOW I'M SEEING THINGS!
IN JUST A MOMENT, HE'LL BE FEELING THINGS!
CLUNG

EEK! MY NOSE!
NOW WE'LL SEE HOW HE LIKES IT!
YANK

ODD-BALL NEVER SAYS MUCH— BUT HE IS CERTAINLY GIVING THAT SCOUNDREL AN 'EARFUL'!
TWEAK
TUG
YEEOW! LEGGO!
WHAT A HELPFUL CHUM YOU HAVE, NOBBY!

Harry's HAUNTED HOUSE

HOW ARE YOU GETTING— OWFF! YOU'VE SCARED OFF THE PLUMBERS, YOU DRATTED GHOST!
WE'RE OFF! GANGWAY!

WATER TANK
YERK! THEY'VE BROKEN THROUGH INTO MY WALL SAFE!
THEY'RE NOT PLUMBERS — LOOK WHAT THEY'VE DONE!

YOU CALL THE POLICE— I KNOW HOW TO STOP THEM FROM GETTING AWAY!

UNDER THE ROAD...
I'LL GET AHEAD OF THEM BY GOING ALONG THIS WATER MAIN!

THEN...
WHOOO! GIVE YOURSELVES UP OR I'LL HAUNT YOU FOREVER!
OH, NO! WE'LL DO ANYTHING — ONLY LEAVE US ALONE!
SCREECH!

WELL DONE, HARRY— I THINK YOU SHOULD GIVE HIM A SLAP-UP FEED, SIR— HE SAVED YOUR LIFE SAVINGS!
YIPPEE!
HUH! I SUPPOSE SO!
£

LAZY Bones

WHERE'S BENNY? HE'S SUPPOSED TO BE HELPING ME IN THE KITCHEN!
SLAM!

YOU USELESS THING! YOU'RE LAZY! IDLE!
THROB!

HUH! I DO WISH YOU'D STOP FUSSING, MUM!
OOH!
ALL RIGHT! I WILL..!

MINUTES LATER...
...BUT I'VE BROUGHT FUSS POT ALONG TO DO IT FOR ME!
DISGRACEFUL, LAZING ABOUT! FUSS! FUSS! YOU SHOULD BE UP HELPING YOUR POOR MOTHER! FUSS! FUSS! FUSS!

GET EVERY SPECK OFF THOSE PLATES! IF I HAVE ONE SINGLE COMPLAINT YOU'LL DO THEM ALL AGAIN! THEN YOU'VE GOT THE DUSTING AND POLISHING TO DO! THEN...
AND THE BEST BIT ABOUT IT IS... IT WAS BENNY WHO GAVE ME THE IDEA!
FLOOR POLISH

SID'S SNAKE

LADIES AND GENTLEMEN! ZIPPO, HE WILL A-NOW MAKE HIMSELF A-VANISH!

A LEETLE SPRINKLE OF MAGIC DUST ON MY A-WAND AND...
SO WHAT'S SO CLEVER? EVEN I CAN DO THAT!
ZAP!

A DIP IN THE MAGIC DUST WITH MY VERY OWN WAND AND I'LL TRY IT ON SID!
NO, SLIPPY! DON'T BE A FOOL!

ZAP!

OOER! THAT'S NOT QUITE RIGHT!
OH, NO! WHAT HAVE YOU DONE?

WHAT HAVE I DONE... WHAT HAVE I DONE..?

WHEW! THANK GOODNESS – I'VE ONLY BEEN WANDERING IN MY DREAMS!
ZZZZ!
MAGIC SET

SWEET-TOOTH

BRRR! NOW WHAT SWEETS CAN I EAT ON A COLD DAY LIKE THIS?
Toffees

OF COURSE! EXTRA-STRONG HOT MINTS! THERE'S ALWAYS SOMETHING FOR A SWEET-TOOTH LIKE ME! CHUCKLE!

NOW FOR A NICE WALK, KEEPING MYSELF WARM BY SUCKING ONE AFTER THE OTHER!
HELLO! THIS LOOKS INTERESTING!

SPLAT!
YERK! WHAT THE..?

HA, HA! YOU'RE A SUCKER ALL RIGHT, SWEET-TOOTH! AND IT'S SNOW USE TRYING TO CATCH ME!
HEY! MY SWEETS!

AHA! GREEDY GREG IS WRONG... I CAN FOLLOW HIS TRAIL OF FOOTPRINTS IN THE SNOW!

HO, HO! I'LL KEEP MY BAG OF SWEETS FOR LATER AND EAT SWEET-TOOTH'S NOW! WONDER WHAT THEY ARE?

GRR! GIVE ME BACK MY BAG OF SWEETS, YOU ROTTER!
WOW! SWEET-TOOTH HAS CAUGHT ME UP!
GRAB!

HE WON'T GET HIS SWEETS, THOUGH! I'LL SCOFF 'EM ALL IN ONE GO! HEE, HEE!
TIP!

HAAAAGH! MY MOUTH IS ON FIRE!
HOT MINTY AIR!
MELT!

HEE, HEE!
SPLOPP!
ERK!

HELP! I CAN'T MOVE!
HO, HO! THAT'S COOLED GREG'S APPETITE! SO HE WON'T GET HEATED IF I TAKE HIS SWEETS IN PAYMENT FOR MINE, WILL HE?
Y. Metcalfe

Joker

IT'S FROSTY TODAY!
SURE IS! SEE THE ICICLES ON OUR GARAGE ROOF, JOKER?

HERE, YOU CAN FEEL ONE!
EH?

OOOOH! EEEEK! BRRRR!
HAW, HAW, HAW!

I'LL PAY YOU BACK FOR THAT, NORMAN NASTY!
HAW, HAW! I'LL BE READY FOR YOU!

PITY THERE ISN'T ANY SNOW! THAT'S ALWAYS GOOD FOR SOME REVENGE JOKES!

BUT...
A JOKER IS NEVER AT A LOSS!
S-SNOWBALLS! B-BUT HOW?
COP THIS LOT!
ERK!
FLING!
FLING!
HUH..?
TAP!
TAP!
PAT!
PAT!
THESE ARE JUST COTTON-WOOL FAKES!
TRUE!
SNIFF!
PONG
PONG!
PING!
PONG!
YEEEEAAARGH!
BUT THEY'RE STUFFED WITH JOKES!

SUPER DAD

BAKER
SPECIALITY-
CUSTARD PIES
FOOH!
THAT POOR BLOKE'S GOT A HEAVY LOAD TO CARRY! HE NEEDS A HAND..!

WHA..?
OR BETTER STILL — A FOOT!
TRIP

BAH! MY 'ORRIBLE OFFSPRING NEEDS A LESSON FROM SUPER DAD!
HEE, HEE!
SPLOT!

AT A CIRCUS...
BACK SOON!
YIPES! MY TROUPE OF ELEPHANTS — FLYING! WHERE'D THEY LEARN THAT TRICK?
AND AFTER OTHER PREPARATIONS...
WHAT ELSE COULD DO SUCH A SUPER JOB OF MIXING MY SUPER CUSTARD PIE?
THIS IS FUN, LADS — TASTES GOOD, TOO!
MIX!
STOMP!
STOMP!

MINUTES LATER...
THE SUN HAS BAKED IT TO A LOVELY TURN! NOW FOR THE PRESENTATION!

I'LL BLOW HIM SOME FUMES TO WHET HIS APPETITE!
PUFF
SUPER PUFF!
WAFT

MMM! SOMETHING SMELLS GOOD...!
LOVELY SMELL

YEEK!
TRIP!

NUUURGH!
SNIGGER! SOMEHOW I DON'T BELIEVE HE'S ENJOYING IT!
SPLOSH!

AND LATER...
TSK! NEVER HAP-PIE UNLESS YOU'RE MIXED UP IN TROUBLE, ARE YOU, SON? ONE OF THESE DAYS THE POLICE WILL BE TRIPPING ALONG HERE TO TAKE YOU INTO CUSTARD-Y!
SPLUTTER!

FUSS POT

YOUR NEWSPAPER IS ALL CREASED! I'M VERY FUSSY ABOUT MY FATHER'S READING MATERIAL ARRIVING IN PERFECT CONDITION!
I-I DON'T MIND!

HEY, NEWSBOY! MY DAD'S PAPER IS CREASED! I INSIST ON ANOTHER COPY!
SORRY, FUSS POT! THAT'S THE LAST ONE!

NEWSAGENT
THEN I'LL GET ANOTHER ONE AT THE SHOP!
LATEST NEWS

I WANT ANOTHER ONE — THIS NEWSPAPER IS CREASED!
SORRY, FUSS POT! I'M SOLD OUT! THERE'S NOTHING I CAN DO TO HELP YOU!
LATEST NEWS

YOU CAN GET YOUR WIFE TO IRON IT!
Y-YES, FUSS POT!
LATEST NEWS

IRONING A NEWSPAPER ! GRRR ! BUT SHE'LL KICK UP SUCH A FUSS IF I DON'T !

NEWS AGENT
SIGH !
HMM ! NOT BAD !
LOCAL NEWS
PARK

HELP ! THE WIND HAS TAKEN IT RIGHT OUT OF MY HANDS !
PARK

HEY ! THAT'S MY DAD'S PAPER !
LITTER

HERE YOU ARE THEN, FUSS POT !

NOW WE ARE ALL CREASED WITH LAUGHTER... EXCEPT YOUR DAD!
GRR ! MY PAPER !

THE SLIMMS

PHONE UP AND GET SOME FOOD DELIVERIES ORGANISED WHILE SAMMY'S BUSY!
I WOULD, BUT HE ALWAYS STOPS OUR GOODIES ARRIVING!

THEN DAD HAD A BRIGHT IDEA...
TEE, HEE! I'LL REMOVE OUR NAMEPLATE AND HAVE THE FOOD SENT TO A DIFFERENT ADDRESS!
SLIMM
7

LATER...
OHO! THAT GROCERY DELIVERY VAN IS SLOWING UP! I'LL BET IT'S COMING HERE! I'LL SOON PUT A STOP TO THAT!
GREENE FOR GROCERIES

HOWEVER...
I WAS WRONG! THE VAN'S GONE PAST AND TURNED DOWN THE LANE!
GREENE FOR GROCERIES

AHA! HERE'S THE PLACE I WAS LOOKING FOR!
SLIMM
7½

SOON...
ANOTHER DELIVERY VAN GOING UP THE LANE!
I. COOK BAKER

THEN...
AH! THIS LOOKS LIKE THE WEIGHT-TRAINING EQUIPMENT I'VE ORDERED FOR MUM AND DAD!

HEY! IT'S GOING RIGHT PAST THE HOUSE, TOO!

MEANWHILE...
JUST LOOK AT THAT LOVELY GRUB WE'VE HAD DELIVERED TO OUR NEW ADDRESS!
AND SAMMY DOESN'T KNOW A THING ABOUT IT!
SLIMM
7½

THEN...
HERE'S THE ADDRESS FOR THIS HEAVY GEAR!

CRASH!

WAAH! OUR LOVELY GRUB... FLATTENED!
SOB! SAMMY GETS THE BETTER OF US EVEN WHEN HE DOESN'T KNOW WHAT'S GOING ON!
TERRY BAVE

CHAMP
YOUTH HALL
PANTO
TONIGHT!
JACK AND THE BEANSTALK
I'M A CHAMPION PANTO STAR, GEORGIE! CAN YOU GUESS WHO I AM?
BEANZ

YOUTH HALL
PANTO
TONIGHT
JACK AND THE BEANSTALK
OOPS!
TRIP!
HO, HO! YOU'VE SPILLED THE BEANS, CHAMP!

GASP! THEY REALLY ARE MAGIC BEANS! ONE'S TAKEN ROOT!
WOW!
SPROUT!

COME ON, GEORGIE! LET'S CLIMB UP!
OOER... YOU KNOW WHAT THE REAL JACK FOUND, CHAMP..!
JACK
AND THE
BEANSTALK

FE-FI-FO-FUM!
PLEASE RING
CLUMP!
CLOMP!
WOW! A GIANT! LET'S HIDE IN THE CASTLE BEFORE HE SPOTS US...!

G-GASP! TOO LATE! HE'S COMING!
THUMP!
THUD

OH, NO! HE'S SLAMMED THE DOOR! WE'RE TRAPPED!
SLAM!

THIS BEAN WILL SAVE US!
HUH..?
Z'ING!
BEANZ

BONK!
TING-A-LING!

'SFUNNY! THERE'S NOBODY THERE!
PLEASE RING
TEE, HEE! THANKS FOR LETTING US OUT, MR. GIANT! MAKE FOR THE BEANSTALK, GEORGIE!
ZOOM!

HO, HO! MADE IT! LUCKY I'M A CHAMPION SHOT—I NEVER MISS!
BUMP!

HO, HO! YES YOU DO, CHAMP! YOU'VE MISSED THE PANTO!
GROAN! I MUST'VE KNOCKED MYSELF OUT WHEN I TRIPPED UP! IT WAS ALL A DREAM!
BEANZ

Tiny Tycoon

PAH! MY TOOL BOX IS FULL OF METAL WASHERS! THEY'RE NO USE TO ANYONE!
I'LL HAVE THEM, DAD!
TOOL BOX

I'M BOUND TO BE ABLE TO MAKE SOME MONEY FROM THESE!
CHINK CHINK

JEWELLERY
ME WANNA NECKLACE, MUM!
THEY'RE ALL TOO EXPENSIVE, DEAR!
AHA! MY FIRST CUSTOMERS!

HOW ABOUT THIS NECKLACE, MISSUS? IT'S GOING CHEAP!
OOH! BUY IT, MUM... PLEASE!

OKAY THEN! I'LL TAKE IT!
COO! LOOK AT ALL THE MONEY THAT KID'S CARRYING! HIS BAG'S BULGING AT THE SEAMS!

I'LL TAKE THAT!
HEY!
SNATCH

GRRR... YOU WON'T GET AWAY WITH THAT, MATE! I HAVEN'T MADE ANY MONEY ON THOSE WASHERS YET!
WHIRL!

THIS'LL STOP YOU!
ERK! CAN'T SEE WHERE I'M GOING!
PLOP!

GOOD WORK, LAD! WE'VE BEEN AFTER THAT THIEF FOR WEEKS!
CRASH.
GNNN!

WE'LL HAVE TO KEEP THIS BAG OF WASHERS AS EVIDENCE! BUT THERE'S A REWARD GOING!
COO! SMASHING! HERE'S YOUR NECKLACE BACK, MISSUS!

SO, LATER...
HI, DAD! I GOT RID OF THOSE WASHERS FOR YOU!
GASP! I DON'T KNOW HOW YOU DO IT, TINY!

LOSER

HELLO, JIMMY, I'VE BEEN SHOPPING FOR MUM, AND I'VE BROUGHT YOU SOME NUTS..!

MUSTN'T HAVE YOU LOSING WEIGHT!

AW, NUTS— NOW I'VE LOST HIM!

HERE'S YOUR SHOPPING, MUM! HAVE YOU SEEN MY PET MOUSE IN HERE? I'VE LOST IT!

NOW I'VE LOST MUM, SHE HASN'T LOST HER FEAR OF MICE YET! HEY, PERHAPS JIMMY WENT OUTSIDE, TOO!
EEEEEK!
WAG
WAG

FANCY CRAWLING ABOUT IN THE SNOW, LOSER, YOU MUST HAVE LOST YOUR SENSES!
I'VE LOST MY PET MOUSE— HAVE YOU SEEN HIM?

WHAT'S HE LOOK LIKE?
HANG ON, I'VE GOT A PENCIL SOMEWHERE, I'LL DRAW YOU A PICTURE!
WAG

HEY, THERE'S NO NEED— HE LOOKS JUST LIKE THIS!
OKAY, I'LL KEEP AN EYE OPEN FOR HIM!

HEY, IT IS YOU, JIMMY, YOU WERE HIDING IN MY POCKET— COME ON, I'M PUTTING YOU BACK IN YOUR CAGE!
WAG
WAG

IT'S ALL RIGHT, MUM, HE'S BACK IN HIS CAGE!
GOOD.. NOW WHERE'S MY CHANGE?

YIKES! THAT PESKY MOUSE MUST HAVE NIBBLED A HOLE IN THE LINING, AND I'VE LOST IT!
GRR! I'M LOSING PATIENCE! FIND IT!

WHAT YOU LOST THIS TIME, THEN, AN ELEPHANT?
AWW! GET LOST!

SAMMY SHRINK

SIGH! I WISH I WASN'T SO SMALL!

YESTERDAY I FELL DOWN A GAP IN THE CRAZY PAVING!
AAAGHHHHHHH!

AND THIS MORNING, THE CAT SAT ON ME AGAIN!
OOOOOFFFFF!

IF ONLY THIS WAS GROWTH TONIC INSTEAD OF LEMONADE...
FIZZY POP

LOOK AT THIS! I'M GROWING BIGGER! FAN-TASTIC!

BUT...
OWWCH! I'VE HIT MY HEAD ON THE CEILING!
KLUNK!
AND...
GLURK! NOW I CAN'T GET OUT OF THE SHED!
THAT'S BETTER!
SHRIEK! A G-G-GIANT!
GET THE ARMY!
CALL THE POLICE!
OKAY! HOLD IT RIGHT THERE!
BUT IT'S ONLY ME — LITTLE SAMMY SHRINK!
THEN...
I SAY, SAMMY! LOOK WHAT I'VE GOT FOR YOU! A GROWTH TONIC!
A WHAT?!
AYEEEEE! N-N-NO! ANYTHING BUT THAT!
I'LL NEVER UNDERSTAND THAT BOY! HE'S ALWAYS WISHING HE WASN'T SO SMALL..!

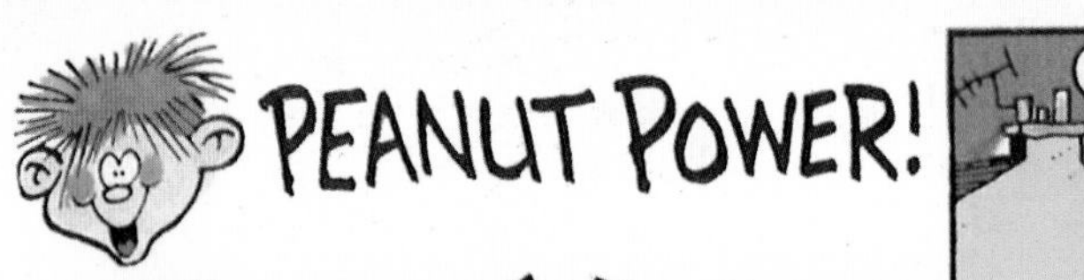
PEANUT POWER!

GUY
GORILLA

SHRIEK!
OH, DEAR!
SCREAM! A M-MONSTER GUG-GORILLA!

CLOSE BY...
HUR, HUR! I'LL CAPTURE THAT GORILLA, AND SELL IT TO THE ZOO! CACKLE!
THOUGHTS OF LOVELY LOOT!
BEST 'NANAS
TOSS!

SNIFF! YUM! BANANAS! MY FAVOURITE!
NOSTRIL- NURDLING NIFF OF 'NANAS!

SLOBBER! DROOL!
CACKLE! THERE HE IS!
IRRESISTIBLE AROMA!

GOT HIM! I'M GOING TO 'PHONE THE ZOO!

TRAP ME, WOULD HE?
TRIUMPH!
WIBBLE! WOBBLE!

THOSE BARS WERE MEANT TO KEEP IN A NINE FOOT GORILLA, NOT A SKINNY KID! HEH, HEH!

YIPES! HE'S GONE! GULP! HOW DID HE ESCAPE?
NOW TO TEACH HIM A LESSON! I'LL HAVE A PEANUT!
WORRIED!
GUZZLE!
PEANUTS

GGGGARRROOOWWLLLUURAGGHH! SNAARRRLL!
EEEEKK! YEEAARRGH! THE GORILLA'S OUT TO GET ME! YELP!

GULP! THERE! SWALLOWED THE KEY! NOW THAT MONSTER CAN'T GET IN TO EAT ME!
CHUCKLE! AN' YOU CAN'T GET OUT!
WIBBLE! WOBBLE!

I DUNNO ABOUT A GORILLA, BUT HE LOOKS WILD ENOUGH!
HE SHOULD ATTRACT A GOOD CROWD! CHUCKLE!
HO, HO! HAVE A BANANA! CHOMP! CHORTLE!
-TOM PATERSON-

STONEAGE JOKES BY
YOU'RE THE LAZIEST MAN I KNOW!
QUICK, OG – PASS ME THE CLUB!
SAY 'HELLO' TO GRANDPA, DEAR!
THERE ARE STILL ONE OR TWO WRINKLES TO IRON OUT!

GO ON! ARE YOU A MAN OR A MOUSE?

I'M SICK OF BRONTOSAUROUS! SICK! SICK! SICK!
HURRY!
ZZZZZ
THE END
JIM CROCKER.

Junior Rotter

SNATCH!
WHY, THANK YOU, SUE HELEN!

SHE DOESN'T OWE ANY MONEY... I'LL RUN FOR IT BEFORE SHE REMEMBERS!

BUT THEN...
HI, J.R.! AREN'T YOU GOING TO THE PARTY?
PARTY? WHERE?
SCREECH!

WHY AT YOUR HOUSE, OF COURSE! SUE HELEN IS ORGANISING IT!

OH, SHE IS, EH? PLAYING A LITTLE ROTTEN TRICK OF HER OWN, TO KEEP ME OUT OF SIGHT, EH?
FLIP!

AND SO...
I'LL TEACH THAT NO-GOOD SISTER OF MINE NEVER TO TRY TO BEAT A ROTTER AT HIS OWN GAME!

TUM-TEE-TUM!

NOW TO WAIT FOR THE FUN TO START!

AND, BEFORE LONG...
AAATCHOOOO! GUROOOO! UGH! BLAH!
HAW! HAW! HAW!

BUT...
J.R.! WHERE IS THAT BOY?
MA! GULP!

I DIDN'T KNOW MA WAS HAVING A PARTY TODAY, AS WELL!
THAT'S WHY MY PARTY IS BEING HELD IN THE GAMES ROOM!

GRR! WHEN I FIND HIM...
PLEASE HIDE ME, SUE HELEN! I'LL BE AS GOOD AS GOLD, I PROMISE!
WELL... FOR THAT DOLLAR YOU OWE ME, I MAY CONSIDER IT!
POP

GINGER'S TUM

HEH, HEH! I LAID MY MITTS ON SOME TASTY GRUB IN THE FOOD STORE! FROZEN FISH AND FRENCH LOAVES!
FOOD STORE

HMM! RECKON WE'LL HELP OURSELVES TO GINGER'S GRUB! SLURP! I'M FEELIN' PECKISH!
OOER!

HEH, HEH! MY FROZEN FISH MAKE GREAT SNOW SHOES... I'LL BE ABLE TO OUT-RUN 'EM EASILY!
PUFF! WHEEZE!

PANT! PUFF! GRR!
ULP! THEY'RE GAINING ON ME! I'LL HAVE TO THINK AGAIN!

TEE, HEE! THIS IS WHAT YOU CALL USING YOUR LOAF! YUK, YUK!
RAGE!

Knight School

NOW WE CAN SKI ON OUR OWN WITHOUT SIR KNIGHT'S BRAGGING! HEH, HEH!
GROAN! OOH!

BUT SOON...
YIPPEEE! THIS IS GREAT FUN!
GRRRR... I'LL STILL SHOW THEM A THING OR TWO!

MY BUILT-IN BULLDOZER WILL DO THE TRICK!
EEK! THE SNOW'S MOVING UPHILL TOWARDS US!

EEK! AAARGH!
A PRACTICE SKI-JUMP WON'T HARM THEM! HEH, HEH!

OOF!
GLUB!
AH! NICE OF YOU TO DROP IN ON ME, KIDS! TEE, HEE!

NOW YOU REALLY CAN HELP ME PRACTICE MY SKI-ING!
EH? H..H..HOW?

YOU MAKE GOOD MARKERS FOR ME TO ZIG-ZAG BETWEEN! HM, HM!
BAH! WE'RE UP TO OUR NECKS IN IT AGAIN!

CHAMP
CHAMP'S DOG

WHAT'S THIS, CHAMP? GOING TO REPAPER YOUR ROOM?
NO, I'M GOING TO BE A PARCEL-WRAPPING CHAMP! YOU KNOW ALL THOSE FUNNY-SHAPED THINGS YOU HAVE TO WRAP AT CHRISTMAS TIME? I'M GOING TO BE ABLE TO WRAP 'EM ALL!
MERRY CHRISTMAS

THAT KENNEL WILL DO FOR A BIT OF PRACTICE!
OKAY— I'LL FETCH IT!
KEEP OUT!
ROVER'S PAD

THAT'S IT— PUT IT DOWN ON THE PAPER!
PHEW! IT'S HEAVY!
CHIP-ITE TWIT OF THE YEAR
SIGNED CHAMP
ROVER'S PAD

SNARRRL!
THERE— HOW'S THAT?
NOT BAD— BUT WHERE'S THAT GROWLING COMING FROM?
WHIZZ-KIDS ARE THE MOST LUVLY, HAPPY BEAUTIFUL KIDS IN THE WORLD AREN'T WE?

RRRIIIPPP!
GURR! GNASH!
ERK! IT'S A PITY YOU WRAPPED THE DOG UP SO WELL, CHAMP!
SAVE YOUR BREATH— RUN!
COR! A GIFT-WRAPPED DOG!
SNAP!

PUFF! PANT! WHEEZE!
WE'VE OUTRUN IT— LET'S NIP UP HERE SO HE WON'T FIND US!
PING!

FOOTBALL CHAMP

HOCKEY CHAMP

CRICKET CHAMP

ATHLETICS CHAMP
TENNIS CHAMP

RUGBY CHAMP

FISHING CHAMP

LOOK — THAT WILL BE A GOOD TEST OF MY WRAPPING SKILL!
COUGH!
PANT!
WHEEZE!
BONK!

HEH, HEH! GOT HIM!
THAT'S THE WAY, ASSISTANT!
TARGET
WHIRR!

YEEHAGH!

GRROWL! SNAP! GNASH!
TIP-TOE!

ERK!
HUR! HUR!
CLUNK!

HEE, HEE! CHAMP'S GETTING CARRIED AWAY WITH HIS WORK!
SNIGGER!
HEEEELP!
COR! A GIFT-WRAPPED CHAMP!
ROLL!

Merry Christmas
KRUMP!
RUMBLE!
RUMBLE!
GAAH!

WELL, THAT WRAPS THAT UP! HAW, HAW!
BAH! I THINK I'LL JUST GIVE YOU SOME WRAPPING PAPER AND KEEP YOUR PRESENT!
CHORTLE! CHORTLE!
SNIGGER!
CHUCKLE!
SCOFF!
GUFFAW!
WAG!
HOP!
HOP! HOP! HOP!

SALT...
MUSTARD...
VINEGAR...
PEPPER...
IT'S OKAY, FRED—IT'S NOT POISONOUS!
Snakes
Snakes alive!
I THINK I'LL BUY HIM A RATTLE FOR HIS BIRTHDAY!
SUBTRACT 4092 FROM 81656!
CAN'T, SIR—I'M AN ADDER!

CHIPS

SHINER SEEING DOUBLE

At first glance all these pictures of Shiner may look alike, but only two are exactly the same. See if you can spot them.

JAILBREAK!
WORKING FROM BRICK TO BRICK, HOW DOES OUR CONVICT GET OVER THE WALL?
OVER!!
WARDER
START HERE
CLIFF BROWN

tiny tycoon

H'MM! I WONDER WHAT I CAN DO WITH THESE INNER-TUBES? NO-ONE SWIMS IN THIS WEATHER SO I CAN'T SELL THEM AS LIFEBELTS!
AND THEY'RE A BIT ON THE BULKY SIDE FOR HOOLA-HOOPS!

GRR! THESE STUPID LITTLE TUBES OF PAINT ARE HOPELESS WHEN ONE IS PAINTING A CANVAS THIS SIZE!
?

FOLLOW ME, SIR! I THINK I MIGHT HAVE THE ANSWER FOR YOU HERE!
?
WHOLESALE PAINT SUPPLIES
PAINT
OPEN
RED
RED
RED

SOON...
SUPERB! MAGNIFICENT!
NOW THESE ARE WHAT I CALL TUBES OF PAINT!
BLUE
SQUEEEZE!
GREEN
WHITE

THANKS, TINY! THIS WILL MAKE CLEANING JUMBO'S TUSKS A LOT EASIER!
ANOTHER LITTLE IDEA OF MINE! ELEPHANTS NEED KING-SIZE TUBES OF TOOTHPASTE! HO, HO!
SQUEEZE!
TOOTHPASTE

OHO! LOOKS AS IF OLD MISTER GREEN IS GOING TO BE LATE FOR HIS TUBE TRAIN AGAIN THIS MORNING!
PUFF!
GASP!
TUBE

LET MY TUBE GET YOU TO YOUR TUBE IN DOUBLE-QUICK TIME, MISTER GREEN!
?
S-T-R-E-T-C-H!

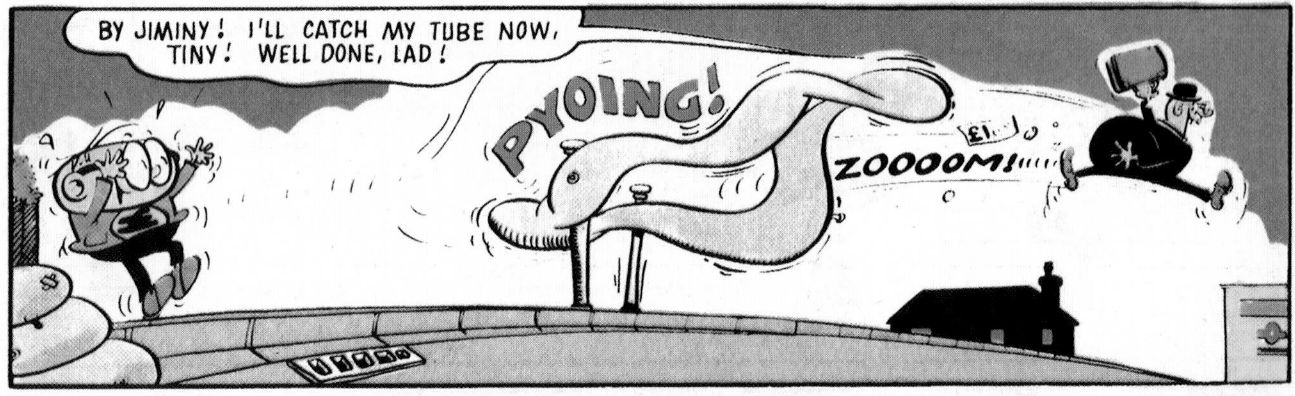
BY JIMINY! I'LL CATCH MY TUBE NOW, TINY! WELL DONE, LAD!
PYOING!
ZOOOOM!

I WONDER HOW I'LL GET RID OF THE REST OF THE TUBES, THOUGH?

BUS STOP
BRR! IT'S TOO COLD TO WALK TODAY, DORIS! LET'S TAKE A BUS!
SHIVER!
TREMBLE
?

NO, BERYL! WE W-WALK! YOU KNOW MISS SKINNER SAYS IT HELPS TO KEEP OUR WEIGHT DOWN!
COO! MAYBE I COULD HELP HERE!
BUS STOP
TREMBLE
SHIVER!

THERE'S LOTS OF LOVELY HOT AIR IN HERE! I'LL BLOW UP THE REST OF MY TUBES WITH IT!
KUNG FU CHINESE LAUNDRY
SOON...
THANKS, TINY! WE WON'T BE COLD WALKING, NOW!
YOU'LL BE AS WARM AS PIE, LADIES – THANKS TO TINY'S INNER GLOW!

SHRIEK!
SLIMLINE CLUB
YOU TWO HAVEN'T BEEN WATCHING YOUR WEIGHT!

OH, YES WE HAVE, MISS SKINNER!

WE AREN'T FAT... IT'S TINY'S PATENT HOT-AIR TUBES! THEY'VE KEPT US LOVELY AND WARM ON THE WAY HERE!
WELL, I NEVER! HO, HO!
HO, HO! IT WASN'T SPARE TYRES...IT WAS MY INNER TUBES!
GLOW!
GLOW!
HEAT!

AND THAT'S ME SOLD OUT, NOW! AT A TIDY PROFIT!
INK

SUPER DAD

BUS STATION THAT WAY, SIR... HOTEL DOWN THERE, MADAM!
I LOVE DIRECTING TWITS LOST IN FOGGY WEATHER! SNIGGER!

WHAT A MIST-ERIOUS ACCIDENT! HUR, HUR!
YEEOW!
NOTICE
DEAD END
BIFF!

YUK, YUK! AND THAT ONE FELL DIRECTLY FOR THE GAG!
NO FISHING
GLOOP!
SPLOOSH!

GOOD THING A SPRY LAD LIKE ME KNOWS HIS WAY BACK HOME!
BUT WEATHER HE MAKES IT A JOB FOR SUPER DAD!

THIS OLD SIGNPOST SHOULD MAKE THAT SON OF MINE SIGH-N!
YANK!

CRUMP!
URF! WHERE'D THAT COME FROM?

SUPER SPIN!
YOU'RE ABOUT TO FIND OUT WHERE IT'S GOING, LAD!
WAAA!

THERE! TAKING THAT WRONG TURNING SHOULD STRIKE THE LESSON HOME!
EE-EE-EEK!
WHIZZZ!

HELP! I'M LOST IN SPACE!
ZWOOOSH!

GEE WHIZZ! A KID'S ARRIVED NOW! WE'LL TAKE HIM BACK WITH US!
USA
?
SPLONK!

SOME TIME LATER...
SEEING YOU'RE SO UNDER THE WEATHER, I WON'T MOON AT YOU FOR BEING LATE HOME, SON! IN A WAY, AN OLD FOG-EY LIKE ME HAS MIST-ED YOU!
DAB!
INC-C-CREDIBLE!

SWEET-TOOTH

NOW FOR THE DIFFICULT PART... GETTING THIS LOT HOME WITHOUT BEING AMBUSHED!
SWEET SHOP

H'MM! I THOUGHT SO! THERE'S GREEDY GREG LYING IN WAIT FOR ME!

TOSS!
THIS IS WHERE MY SCOTTISH BLOOD COMES IN HANDY!

YAAAAAGH!
WELL, THAT PUTS PAID TO GREG! HOOTS MON... IF YOU'LL EXCUSE THE SCOTTISH JAR-GON!

H'MM! THE REST OF THE COAST SEEMS TO BE CLEAR! CAN'T SEE ANYONE ELSE ABOUT!

BUT...
I'LL TAKE YOU FOR A RIDE!

SUFFERING SHERBETS! I'VE BEEN AMBUSHED FROM BELOW!
HO! HO! HO!

THIS IS AN EMERGENCY! I'D BETTER DIAL 999... FIRE DIVISION!

ONE FIREMAN COMING UP... OR IS IT DOWN?

NOW I'LL PUT OUT THIS BRIGHT SPARK!
YAAAGH!

WELL, THAT'S THE... ER... FIRE OUT FOR THE COUNT! NOW TO GO HOME AND SCOFF THE GOODIES!
DAZE!

The SLIMMS

THEATRE
THE GREAT HIPPO HYPNOTIST SUPREME
ALL THIS WEEK
YEOW! MAYBE WE COULD GET HIM TO HYPNOTISE SAMMY AND MAKE HIM UNLOCK THE PANTRY DOOR, MUM!

SOMEONE ELSE SAW THE SIGN—SAMMY!
THEAT
THE GREAT HIPPO HYPNOTIST SUPREME
GOSH! MAYBE HE CAN HYPNOTISE MUM AND DAD INTO STOPPING THEM EATING!

LATER...
TRING! TRING!
STAY THERE, SAMMY! THAT'LL BE FOR US!
NO! IT'LL BE FOR ME!

AH! THERE YOU ARE, SIR! COME ON IN!
AMAZING! BOTH MY CLIENTS LIVE IN THE SAME HOUSE!

I PAID YOU TO HYPNOTISE THEM, SIR!
WE PAID YOU TO HYPNOTISE HIM, SIR!
PITY ONLY TO EARN ONE FEE...I'LL HYPNOTISE BOTH PARTIES!

YOU ARE UNDER MY SPELL! YOU WILL OPEN THE PANTRY DOOR!
YOU ARE UNDER MY SPELL! YOU DON'T FEEL HUNGRY!

LARDER
HO, HO! WHILE THEY'RE ALL UNDER MY SPELL, I'LL SCOFF THE GRUB! WHAT A CAPER!

DROOL! MY FAVOURITES! GINGER SNAPS!

OH, NO! I'VE SNAPPED THEM OUT OF THE SPELL!
SNAP!
SNAP!

YAAGH! HE'S EATING ALL THE FAMILY NOSH, SAMMY!
G-GULP!

POLICE
HO, HO! NOW THE GREAT HIPPO KNOWS WHAT IT'S LIKE TO BE IN FOR A SPELL!

IMAGINE THAT FOOL THINKING HE COULD TRICK US!
INDEED, SAMMY! HE SHOULD HAVE KNOWN BETTER! CHOMP!
YIKE! I DON'T BELIEVE IT!

Odd-Ball

NO! I'M NOT RETURNING YOUR BALL! I'M PUTTING IT IN MY SHED WITH ALL THE OTHERS!
THAT ROTTEN OLD MEANY NEVER GIVES US OUR BALLS BACK!

HEY, ODD-BALL! DON'T GO OVER THERE!
YOU'VE HAD THAT, NOBBY!

IN IT GOES...AND...OW! THE LITTLE HORRORS! ANOTHER ONE!
BOMPH!

RIGHT! IN YOU GO, TOO!

SLAM!
CLICK!

THEY'LL NEVER SEE THOSE BALLS AGAIN!

OOOH! AAGH! THEY'VE ESCAPED!

I DON'T KNOW HOW IT HAPPENED! BUT I'M PUTTING THEM ALL BACK IN THE SHED!

FUNNY- MY SHED WAS HERE A MOMENT AGO!

AAAGH! IT'S CHASING ME!

I'LL NEVER CLIMB OVER THE WALL CARRYING THIS LOT! I'LL HAVE TO GET RID OF THEM!

GOOD OLD ODD-BALL!

SHINER
OOH, HENRY! I CAN SEE SHINER! HE'S STARTING A FIGHT! STOP HIM!
RIGHTO, LUV!

PHEW — JUST IN TIME! YOU KNOW WE TOLD YOU NOT TO GET A BLACK EYE TODAY OF ALL DAYS... WHEN YOUR GRANDPARENTS ARE HERE!

I STOPPED HIM, LUV!
GOOD! NOW, SHINER, COMB YOUR HAIR AND TIDY YOURSELF UP... GRANDPA WANTS TO TAKE A PHOTO OF YOU!

HERE HE IS, GRANDPA, ALL NEAT AS A NEW PIN!

SMILE, SHINER! THINK OF SOMETHING NICE!
SMILE, SON!
SAY CHEESE!

LATER, WHEN THE PHOTO WAS PRINTED...
H'MM! NOT A BAD LIKENESS... BUT... BUT... SOMEHOW, IT'S NOT OUR LITTLE SHINER!
HERE, LAD! GIVE ME YOUR PAINT-BRUSH!

LOVELY! PERFECT! THAT'S MORE LIKE OUR LITTLE SHINER!

SHINER'S SILENT SMILES!
NO FISHING BEYOND THIS POINT
BEWARE OF THE DOG
1
2
3
TAKE NOTICE
TAKE NOTICE
TAKE NOTICE
CAT FOOD
CAT FOOD

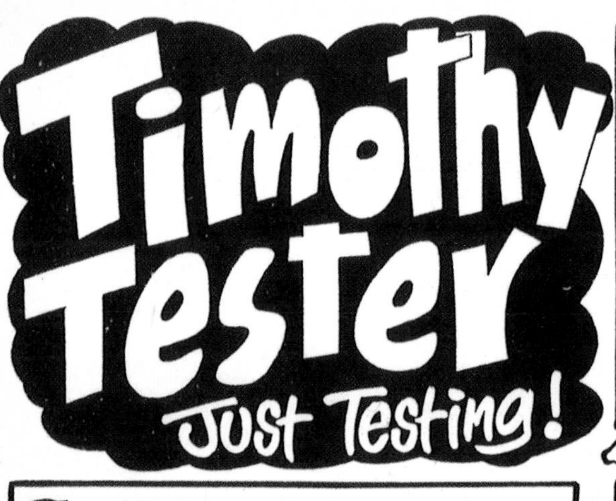

Timothy Tester
Just Testing!

1
WHAT ANIMAL DOES A KETTLE REMIND YOU OF ?

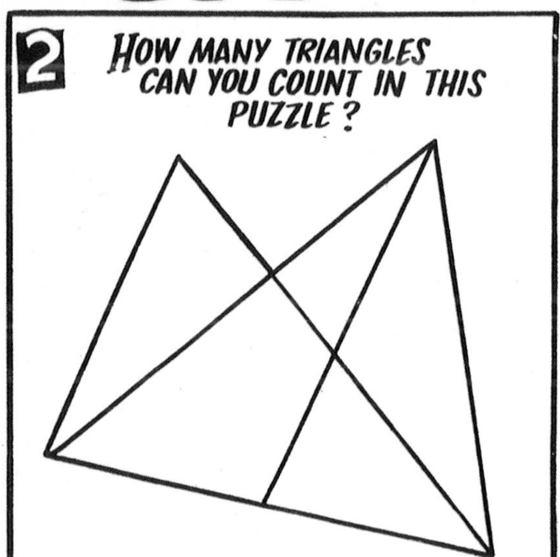

2
HOW MANY TRIANGLES CAN YOU COUNT IN THIS PUZZLE ?

3
BY MOVING TWO MATCHES, CAN YOU MAKE FOUR SQUARES ?

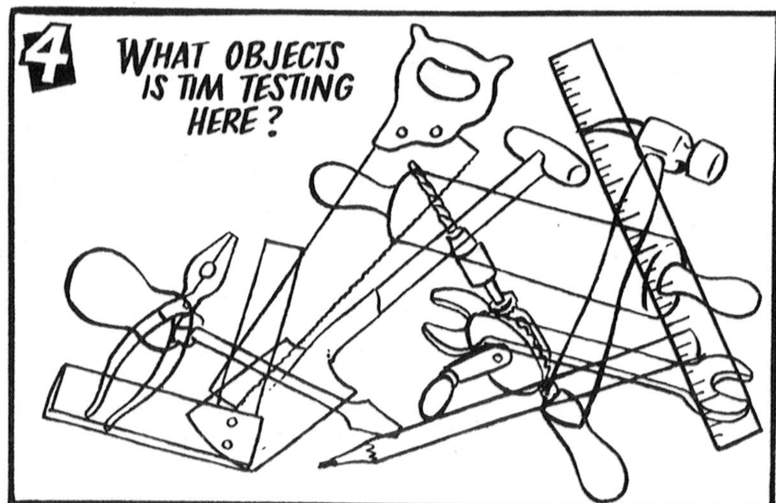

4
WHAT OBJECTS IS TIM TESTING HERE ?

5
WHICH THREE-LETTER WORD WILL COMPLETE ALL THESE WORDS ?
DEE_ _ _
_ _ _CE
DE_ _ _D
S_ _ _T
_ _ _CIL

6
HOW DO YOU TAKE ONE FROM FOUR AND LEAVE FIVE ?

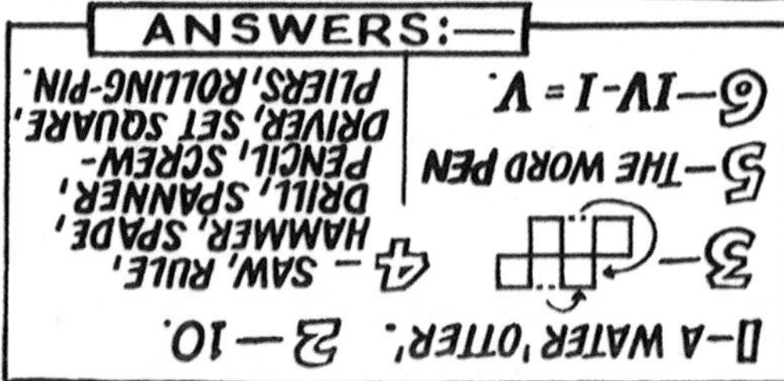

ANSWERS:—
1—A WATER 'OTTER'. 2—10.
3—
4—SAW, RULE, HAMMER, SPADE, DRILL, SPANNER, PENCIL, SCREW-DRIVER, SET SQUARE, PLIERS, ROLLING-PIN.
5—THE WORD PEN
6—IV-I = V.

Junior Rotter

...TO SNEAK UP AND GET A FREE LOOK AT THE LATEST VIDEO FILMS!

BUT...
WHAT ARE YOU UP TO? VAMOOSE... PRONTO!
DARN IT..! RUMBLED! TIME I WASN'T HERE!

LATER...
TICKLE!

OUCH!
OW! MY TOES!
CRUMP!
CRUSH!

ISN'T THAT THE KID WHO STOLE MY BOBBY'S SWEETS?
PARK

EASY TO ESCAPE WITH THE HELP OF OUR TREE!

HO, HO! CAN'T CATCH ME NOW!

BUT...
CRACK!
ERK!

GULP!
SERVES YOU RIGHT!

SO, BACK HOME...
GULP! ER, IT MIGHT GROW A BIT IF WE PLANT IT, PA..!
J.R.! OUR TREE! I'LL..., I'LL...!

OH, PERFECT, J.R.! HOW CLEVER OF YOU!
EH?

JUST RIGHT TO DECORATE OUR CHRISTMAS CAKE!
PHEW! THAT WAS CLOSE! BUT I'D SOMEHOW BETTER FIND A REPLACEMENT TREE BEFORE CHRISTMAS DAY... AND I WILL!

SID'S SNAKE

I'LL NEVER BUILD THIS SNOWMAN IN TIME FOR THE COMPETITION! YOU'LL HAVE TO HELP ME, SLIPPY!
AND LATER...
HUH! THESE SNOWMEN ARE ALL MUCH THE SAME... RATHER BORING!
JUDGE
SNOWMAN COMPETITION
NOW THAT'S WHAT I CALL A NOVELTY SNOWMAN! HE GETS FIRST PRIZE!
BRRRRR! IT'S C-C-COLD IN HERE.. I'M G-G-GOING TO SNEEZE....
SHIVER!
TREMBLE!

A-TISH—OOO!
THAT'S CHEATING— YOU'RE SUPPOSED TO BUILD THE SNOWMAN ON YOUR OWN— NO PRIZE!
I COULDN'T HELP IT!

The "ANNUAL" FOOTBALL MATCH BETWEEN THE "WHIZZ-KIDS" and the "CHIP-ITES"!
WELL! OUR SIDE'S NEARLY ALL HERE...BUT I CAN ONLY SEE ONE CHIP-ITE PLAYER!
1

...AND THAT WAS HOT ROD!
YUK, YUK! THE REST OF THE SIDE'S UNDER MY SMOKE-SCREEN!
YUK, YUK!
2

...THEN SLIPPY CAME TO THE RESCUE...
OY! REF! FOUL! SLIPPY'S TRIPPED US ALL UP!
5

ALL EXCEPT CHIP-ITE WEAR-'EM-OUT WILF... HE JUMPED OVER SLIPPY AND HEADED FOR THE WHIZZ-KIDS' GOAL...
6

BOOMP
WHAT A KICK... IT'LL GO RIGHT INTO THE CHIP-ITE GOAL!
10

BUT BATTY BAT LUCKILY GOT IN THE WAY!
BONK
GOOD OLD BATTY! HE'S HEADED IT BACK AT THE WHIZZ-KID GOAL!
11

...and the final score O-O

THE WINTERLAND RACE GAME

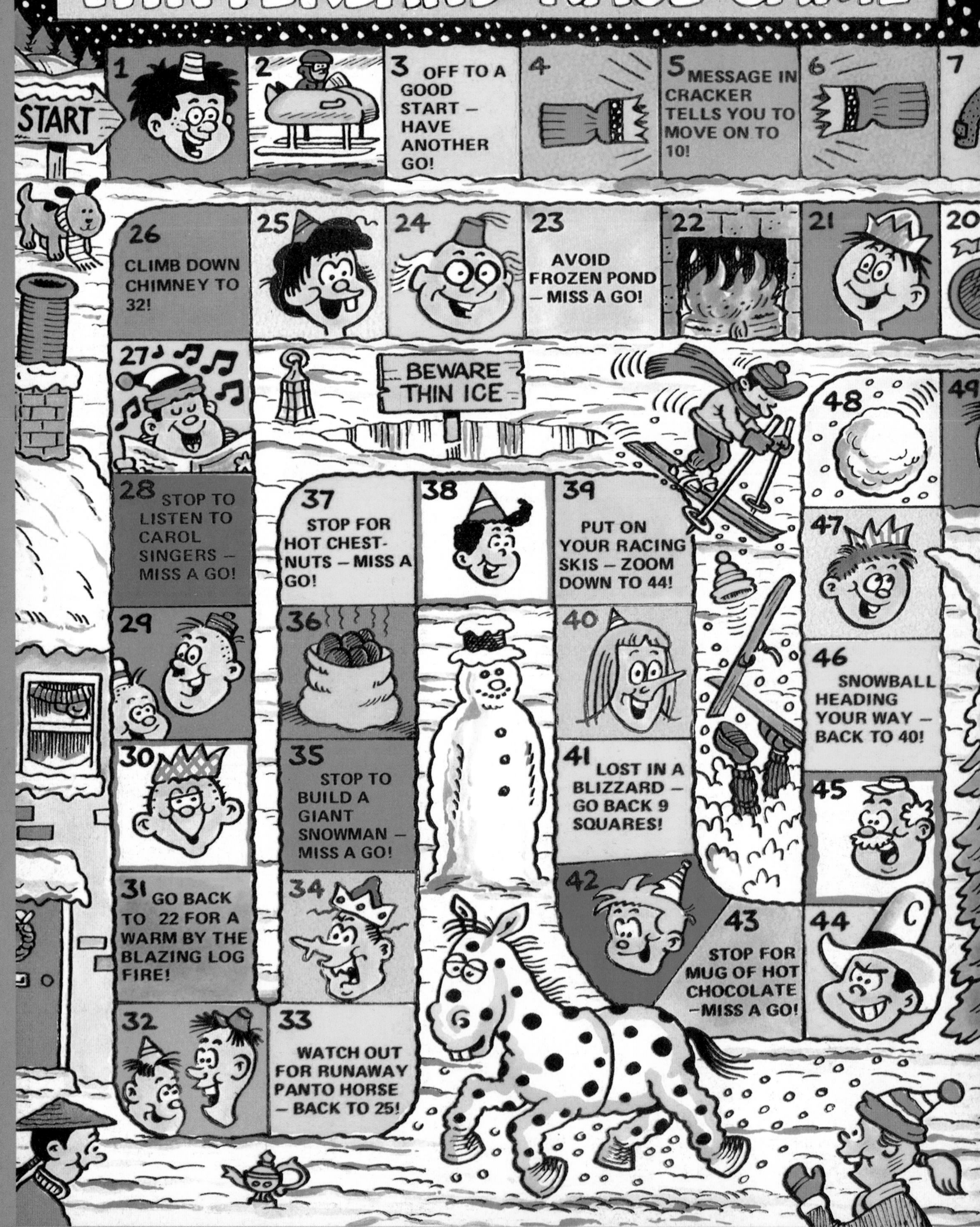